Name

_____

Age

_____

My favourite character is

Lightning
_____

LIGHTYEAR 1st TO THE FINISH!

ANNUAL 2011

EGMONT
We bring stories to life

First published in Great Britain 2010 by Egmont UK Limited,
239 Kensington High Street, London W8 6SA

Editor: Jude Exley. Designer: Jo Bestall

ISBN 978 1 4052 5262 1
1 3 5 7 9 10 8 6 4 2
Printed in Italy

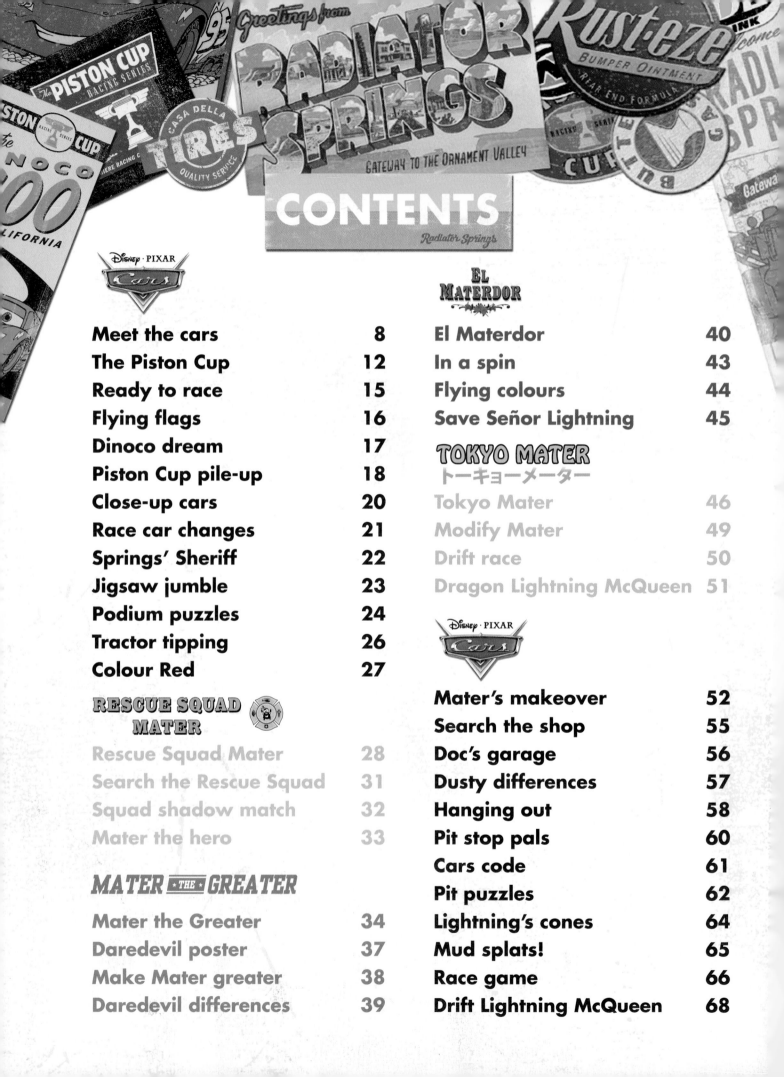

CONTENTS

Radiator Springs

Hello racing fans!

Welcome to this
super-charged annual.
Inside you can read Mater's Tall
Tales, play fun games and enjoy
lots more revved-up action.
Fasten your seatbelt and
enjoy the ride!

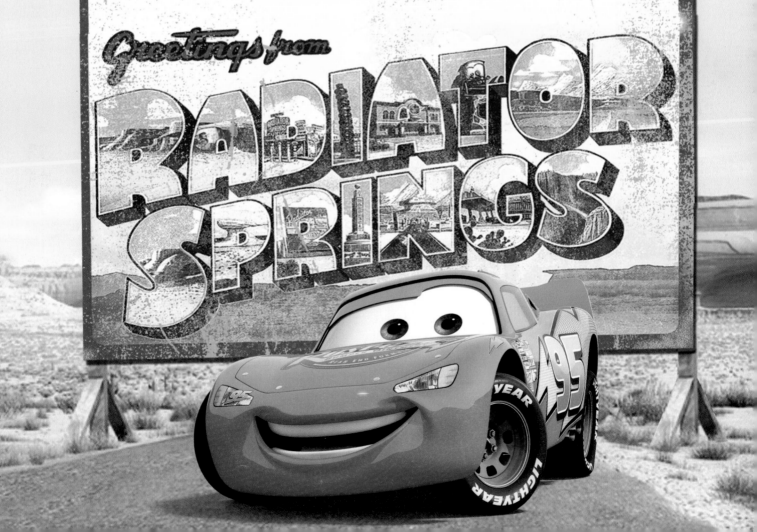

Greetings from RADIATOR SPRINGS

Lightning McQueen

is a hotshot rookie race car who hopes to win the Piston Cup and get sponsorship from Dinoco. But, in the final race of the season, Lightning finishes in a three-way tie with The King and Chick Hicks! On his way to the decider race, Lightning gets lost in a little town called Radiator Springs. There, he makes some new friends who teach him that there's more to life than winning races.

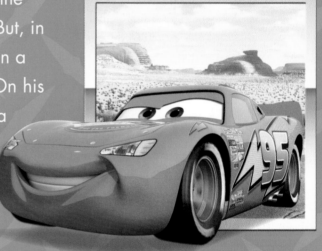

Mater

is a loveable tow truck with a big heart and a sunny nature who is always the first to lend a helping hand. He quickly becomes Lightning's best friend when he arrives in Radiator Springs, though Mater is everything Lightning is not!

Sally Carrera

is a beautiful sports car from California who grew tired of life in the fast lane and made a new start in Radiator Springs and now she wants to put it back on the map. When Sally arrived she quickly fell in love with the town, and when Lightning arrives he soon falls in love with Sally!

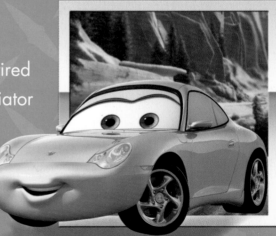

Sheriff

was the first Radiator Springs resident to meet Lightning when he caught him speeding through the town. He takes his job very seriously, but enjoys taking the occasional nap behind the Radiator Springs billboard.

Doc Hudson

is a seemingly quiet country doctor and judge, but he was once a famous race car who won three Piston Cups. He left the racing scene after a terrible crash and moved to Radiator Springs. Doc sees a lot of himself in rookie race car Lightning McQueen.

Sarge

is a patriotic veteran jeep who can often be found manicuring his lawn when he isn't busy running the local army surplus store.

Fillmore

is a hippie Volkswagen bus who lives next door to Sarge and brews organic fuel. The cars bicker constantly, but they can't live without each other!

Ramone

owns the Ramone's House of Body Art, where he paints himself and other cars. He even gives Lightning a new look! Ramone is married to Flo, whose café is next door to his store.

Flo

owns and runs the V8 Cafe, the only gas diner for miles around, where she serves the "finest fuel in fifty states."

Red

is a gentle giant; a big, strong fire engine. He is shy and emotional, often bursting into tears and hiding. Red spends most of his time gardening and washing things!

Luigi & Guido

Luigi is a huge Ferrari fan and has followed racing his entire life. He runs a tyre shop called Casa Della Tires with Guido, his assistant and best friend. The only language Guido can speak and understand fluently is Italian.

Mack

is an experienced trucker and Lightning's trusted driver. He is willing to push the limits of his own sanity and sleep to get Lightning wherever he needs to go. He's a positive guy with a loyal heart and Lightning's one true friend in the racing world.

The King

is a racing legend who has won more Piston Cups than any other car in history, but he knows that it takes more than trophies to make a champion. The King is planning to retire at the end of the season and hand over his sponsorship with Dinoco. Lightning would give just about anything to fill his treads.

Chick Hicks

has spent his career coming second to "The King", but he is determined to do whatever it takes to win the Piston Cup and the legendary Dinoco sponsorship. The only thing standing in his way is Lightning McQueen.

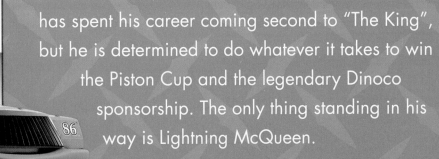

The Piston Cup

1. Young racing car, Lightning McQueen, dreamed of winning the Piston Cup. The little red car also longed for fame and fortune.

2. Today, all of Lightning's dreams could come true! Thousands of cars had gathered to watch the race. He was up against The King and Chick.

3. Lightning was quick and he looked sure to win the race. Chick was jealous and would do anything to beat him, even if it meant cheating.

4. So, Chick caused a big pile-up on the track. He was sure Lightning's race was over. However, Lightning zoomed out of the wreckage, without even a scratch!

5. Lightning was nearly at the finish line, when all of his tyres burst. Chick and The King caught up with him and they crossed the line together.

6. The race was tied and so another race would be held to find a winner. Lightning's driver, Mack, drove through the night to reach the next race.

7. Mack was so tired, though, that he didn't notice when Lightning got separated from him. Lightning became lost and he was scared.

8. Lightning sped into the little town of Radiator Springs, where he lost control and crashed into everything in his path. Finally, he was stopped by Sheriff.

9. Lightning was in a whole heap of trouble. He had ruined the town's main street and the residents of Radiator Springs were not happy.

10. Doc Hudson, the town judge, told Lightning that he must fix the street before he could leave. Would Lightning make it to the next race on time?

The end

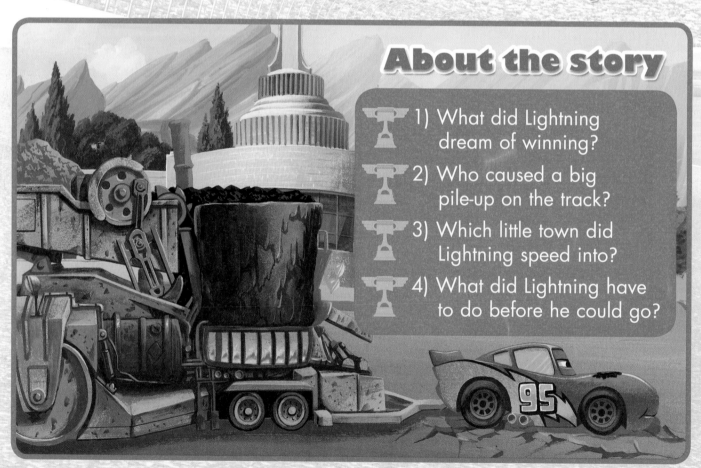

About the story

1) What did Lightning dream of winning?

2) Who caused a big pile-up on the track?

3) Which little town did Lightning speed into?

4) What did Lightning have to do before he could go?

Answers: 1) The Piston Cup. 2) Chick. 3) Radiator Springs. 4) Fix the street.

Ready to race

Lightning has arrived!
Trace over the pale blue lines
and then add some colour.

How many yellow lights
can you count below?
Write your answer
in the box.

Flying flags

Join these racing fans and
answer these quick questions!

1 Which cars are on the big screens? Now colour them in!

2 How many of each colour flag can you count? Write your answers in the boxes.

Answers: 1) Lightning and The King, 2) Red = 6, blue = 5, yellow = 4.

Dinoco dream

It's Lightning's dream to win the Piston Cup.
Can you help him find the right route through this maze,
collecting the Piston Cup on the way?

Colour
the Piston
Cup!

Start

Finish

Piston Cup pile-up

There's a pile-up on the race track. Quickly answer these questions before anyone else crashes!

1 How many cars have crashed?

2 What colour is car 76?
Tick the correct box.

✓ purple   yellow

3 Which of the numbers below is written on the blue car?
Tick the correct box.

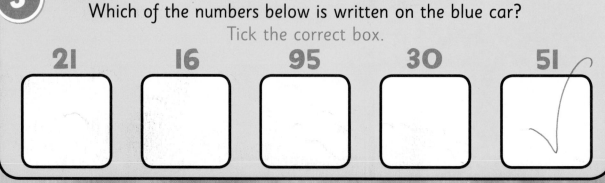

21   16   95   30   51 ✓

18

Answers: 1) 5. 2) Purple. 3) 51. 4) Zoom. 5) The tyre is in the air above the purple car.

Close-up cars

How quickly can you match the close-ups below to the cars on the right? We've done the first one for you.

Write your answers in the circles below.

Race car changes

Lightning McQueen is a famous race car!
Can you spot five changes in the bottom picture?

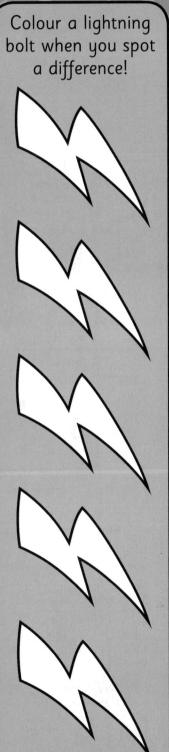

Colour a lightning bolt when you spot a difference!

Springs' Sheriff

Radiator Springs' Sheriff is on the lookout! Give him some colour.

What colour are the cacti on the billboard? Colour this box the same colour.

Answer: Green.

Jigsaw Jumble

Can you complete this Cars jigsaw by matching the pieces at the bottom of the page to the spaces below?

23

Podium puzzles

The Piston Cup race was a three-way tie!
Can you answer these quick questions in time for the re-match?

Colour the race cars!

DINOCO 400

PISTON CUP

1 Who is in the middle of the podium?

2 What numbers are Chick Hicks and The King?

Chick Hicks   The King

Answers: 1) Lightning 2) Chick Hicks = 86, The King = 43. 3) Green. 4) A red flag. 5) Detail c.

3 What colour appears twice in this group of cars?

4 What colour flag is the big camper van waving?

5 Which detail is not from the scene? Tick the box.

a

b

c

d

Tractor tipping

Lightning and Mater are tipping the tractors that add up to 10!
Do the sums to find out who they will tip.
Write your answers in the boxes.

a) 6+4 = 10

b) 5+3 = 8

c) 5+5 = 10

d) 6+2 = 8

e) 7+3 = 10

f) 3+3 = 6

Colour Red

Red, the fire truck, loves watering the flowers!
Add some bright colours.

How many flowers is
Red watering?
Write the number in
the box.

4

RESCUE SQUAD MATER

1. One day, Lightning and Mater were going for a drive. They had just passed Red at the Fire Station when Mater said, "I used to be a fire truck."

2. "What?" asked Lightning. His best friend was a tow truck! Then Mater began to tell him the story of Rescue Squad Mater ...

3. At the Fire Station, Mater was ready for action. An emergency call came in that there was a fire at the old gasoline and match factory!

4. Mater was on his way! "Nee Nah!" He raced down the street. The police and a crowd of cars were waiting for him outside the factory.

5. "Make room for Mater," said the police. "We're counting on you." "I'm on it," said Mater, hosing down the burning building.

6. In Radiator Springs, Lightning said, "Mater, I cannot believe that you were a fire truck." Mater replied, "You remember, you were there too."

7. Back at the factory, Lightning could be seen at an upstairs window. "Help! Help!" he cried. "Remain calm," replied Mater.

8. He hosed Lightning down, then rescued him from the window just before there was a big explosion! Rescue Squad Mater was a hero!

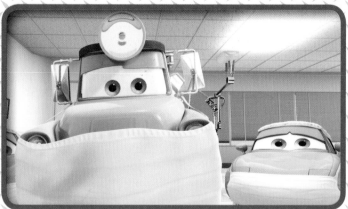

9. Lightning was rushed to hospital. In the operating theatre, he was very surprised to find out that Mater was also a doctor!

10. "Well, what happened?" asked Lightning. "I saved your life," replied Mater. "You didn't," said Lightning. "Did so," replied Mater …

The end

ABOUT THE STORY

1 What vehicle was Rescue Squad Mater?

2 Where was the fire?

3 Who was trapped in the building?

4 Who was the doctor?

Answers: 1) A fire truck. 2) The old gasoline and match factory. 3) Lightning McQueen. 4) Mater.

SEARCH THE RESCUE SQUAD

These close-ups can all be found in the big picture.
Circle them when you have found them.

SQUAD SHADOW MATCH

Draw lines to match the Rescue Squad to their shadows.

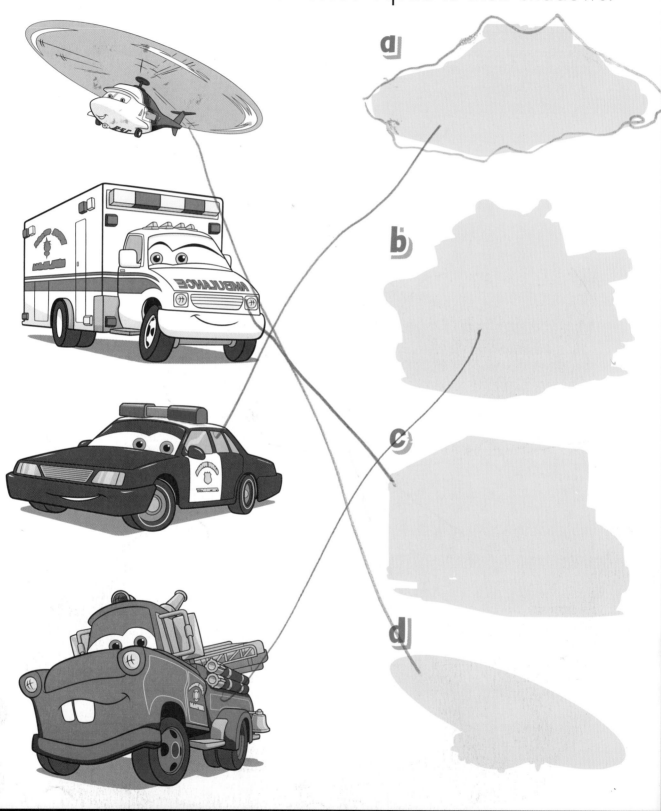

a)

b)

c)

d)

Answers: a) Trooper b) Mater. c) Ambulance. d) Helicopter.

MATER THE HERO

Starting at number 1, join the dots to see what Mater is doing.

Answer: Mater is spraying water from his hose.

MATER THE GREATER

1. One day, Mater was trying to jump a homemade ramp outside Flo's café when he missed.
"Mater, are you ok?" asked Lightning.

2. "Oh shoot, that was nothing,"said Mater. "I used to be a daredevil."
"What?" asked Lightning.
"They called me Mater the Greater …"

3. In the arena, Mater the Greater was going to make his latest daredevil leap across a line of cars. The crowd went wild for their hero!

4. Mater drove up to the ramp ready to take his leap. The drum roll began. He revved up his engine and raced up the ramp, then …

5. Mater landed on the first two cars! "Excuse me, coming through," he said, driving over all the cars to the podium. "He did it!" cheered the crowd.

6. Then there was the time Mater became a cannonball and jumped through a ring of fire. And the time he jumped from the high dive board ...

7. "I busted nearly every part of my body," said Mater. "But the biggest stunt Mater the Greater ever did was jumping Carburettor Canyon."

8. "Jumping Carburettor Canyon, no way!" said Lightning. "Yes way," replied Mater. "You remember, you were there too."

9. "What?" cried Lightning. Then he saw he was at the top of Carburettor Canyon. "Ready buddy," said Mater. And the pitties pushed Lightning off the canyon!

10. Lightning went flying through the air and hurtled to the ground. "What happened?" asked Lightning, back in Radiator Springs. "You didn't make it," replied Mater.

The end

MATER ★ THE ★ GREATER

ABOUT THE STORY

1 What was Mater's daredevil name?

2 What did he jump through?

3 What was Mater's biggest stunt?

4 Who was there with him?

Answers: 1) Mater the Greater. 2) A ring of fire. 3) Jumping Carburettor Canyon. 4) Lightning McQueen.

DAREDEVIL POSTER

Every daredevil needs his own poster.
Design your own Mater the Greater poster.

★ MAKE MATER GREATER ★

Make Mater look greater by adding some daredevil colours.

DAREDEVIL DIFFERENCES

Can you spot 5 differences in picture 2 before Lightning McQueen speeds away? Colour a star each time you spot a difference.

Answers: 1) A headlamp is missing. 2) His eyes have moved. 3) The lightning flash is a different colour. 4) A rocket is missing. 5) The stars are missing.

EL MATERDOR

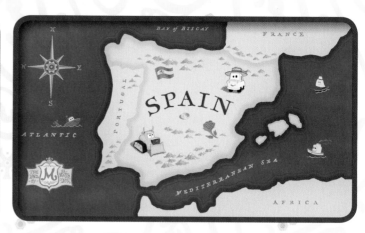

1. One sunny day, Lightning and Mater were driving by a field of bulldozers. "They're just like the ones I used to fight," said Mater.

2. "What?" asked Lightning. "I was a famous bulldozer fighter in Spain," replied Mater. "They called me El Materdor ..."

3. In Spain, El Materdor was in the ring. The doors opened and a bulldozer charged at him! El Materdor swerved and the bulldozer missed him. "Olé!"

4. The bulldozer was furious and he charged at El Materdor again. But this time he didn't miss and he bulldozed him into the ground!

5. The crowd began to weep, but El Materdor was alive! He dusted himself down, then he fought three bulldozers and won. "Olé!" he cried.

6. "Bravo, Señor Mater," said señoritas Mia and Tia. The crowd threw roses for El Materdor. But soon there were bulldozers all around him.

7. "What did you do?" asks Lightning. "Don't you remember, you were there too," replied Mater. "They sure liked that red paint job of yours!"

8. Now Lightning McQueen was in the ring. He was surrounded by bulldozers. Suddenly they charged and chased him around the ring.

9. "Mater, that did not happen," said Lightning. "Try telling that to those bulldozers," replied Mater. And Lightning realised they were surrounded by them!

10. He raced off at full speed as the bulldozers charged after him. Mater was alone. Then Mia and Tia appeared, "Señor Mater" they said. "Señoritas. Olé!" he replied.

The end

El **MATERDOR MAGNIFICO**

¡OLÉ! ¡OLÉ! ¡OLÉ!

ABOUT THE STORY

1 What did Mater do in Spain?

2 Who were his biggest fans?

3 How many bulldozers did he defeat?

4 Who joined him in the ring?

Answers: 1) He was a famous bulldozer fighter. 2) Señoritas Mia and Tia. 3) He fought three bulldozers. 4) Señor Lightning McQueen.

In a spin

Mater has a famous bulldozer fighter name.
Can you find it hidden in the word wheel?

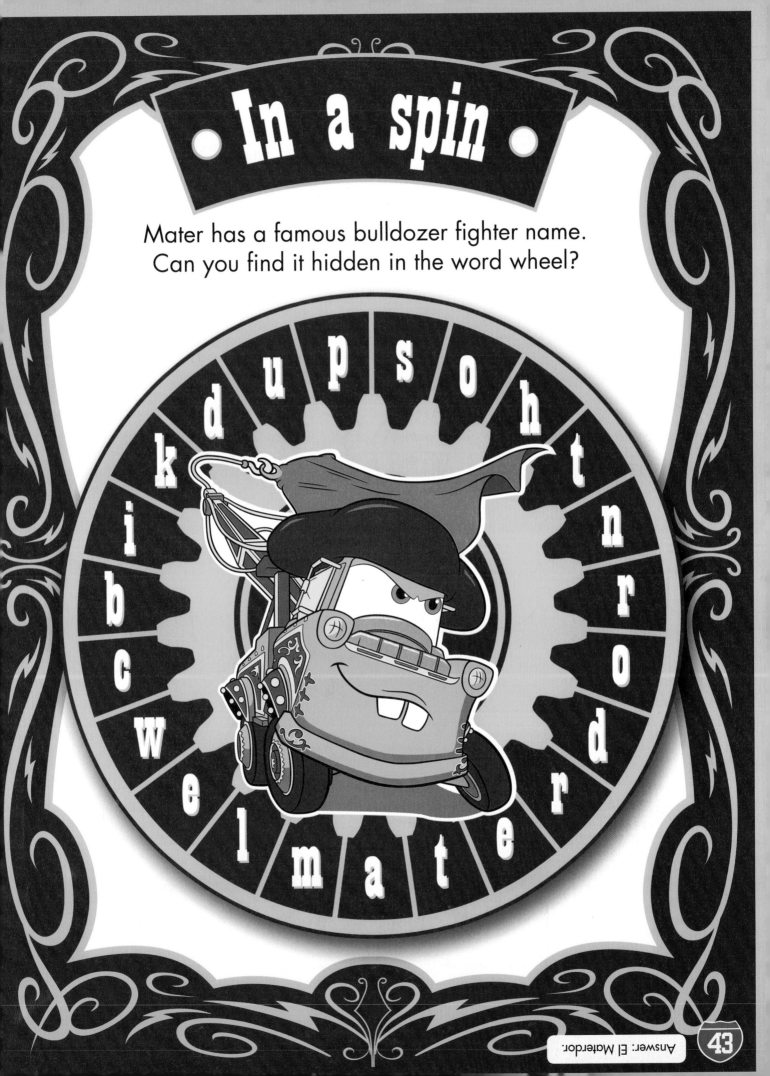

FLYING COLOURS

Colour in the picture of El Materdor using the smaller picture as a guide.

¡OLÉ! ¡OLÉ! ¡OLÉ!

SAVE SEÑOR LIGHTNING

Can you show Lightning the quickest way through the maze to escape the angry bulldozers?

トーキョーメーター
TOKYO MATER

1. It was a quiet morning in Radiator Springs until two cars raced through. "Get back here you import punks," said Sheriff, chasing after them.

2. "I used to be an import," said Mater. "What? No way!" said Lightning. "Yes way," said Mater. "It all started when I met a car who needed a tow…"

3. The car said he was from very far away. But Mater insisted 'no tow is too far for Tow Mater'. So Mater towed the car to Tokyo!

4. In Tokyo, Mater accidentally bumped into Kabuto. He was angry and challenged him to a drift race. But first, Mater had to be modified!

5. Tokyo Mater reappeared with blue paintwork and upgrades! The race was to the top of Tokyo Tower. The winner would be King of all Drifters!

6. The cars were off, and Kabuto was winning. "You can't drift, you're a loser," he said. But then, Tokyo Mater drifted by accident and he took a short cut.

7. Now Tokyo Mater was level with Kabuto. But Kabuto called for his gang of ninjas, then he raced off leaving Tokyo Mater with ninjas on all sides!

8. "Ninjas! What did you do?" asked Lightning. "Well you oughta know," said Mater, "you were there too." And Dragon Lightning McQueen appeared!

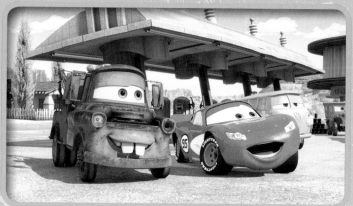

9. He karate kicked the ninjas! Then Tokyo Mater drifted, flew through the air and used his tow hook to reach the top of Toyko Tower first!

10. "That's how I became Tokyo Mater, King of all Drifters," said Mater. "That did not happen," said Lightning. "Oh, yeah, says you," replied Mater.

The end

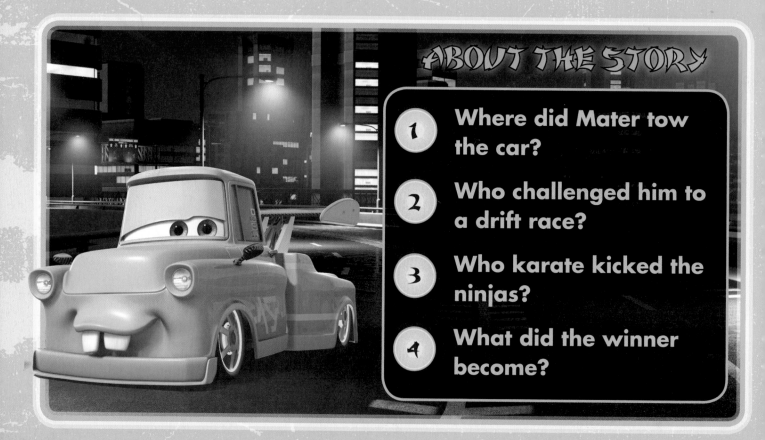

ABOUT THE STORY

1 Where did Mater tow the car?

2 Who challenged him to a drift race?

3 Who karate kicked the ninjas?

4 What did the winner become?

Answers: 1) Tokyo. 2) Kabuto. 3) Dragon Lightning McQueen. 4) King of all Drifters.

Modify Mater

Tokyo Mater was modified with blue paint. Colour in the picture to create your own modified Mater.

DRIFT RACE

Tokyo Mater and Kabuto are racing to the top of Tokyo Tower. Follow the lines to find out who will become the King of all Drifters.

Answer: Tokyo Mater is the King of all Drifters.

One of these pictures of Dragon Lightning McQueen is different from the rest. Can you spot the odd one out?

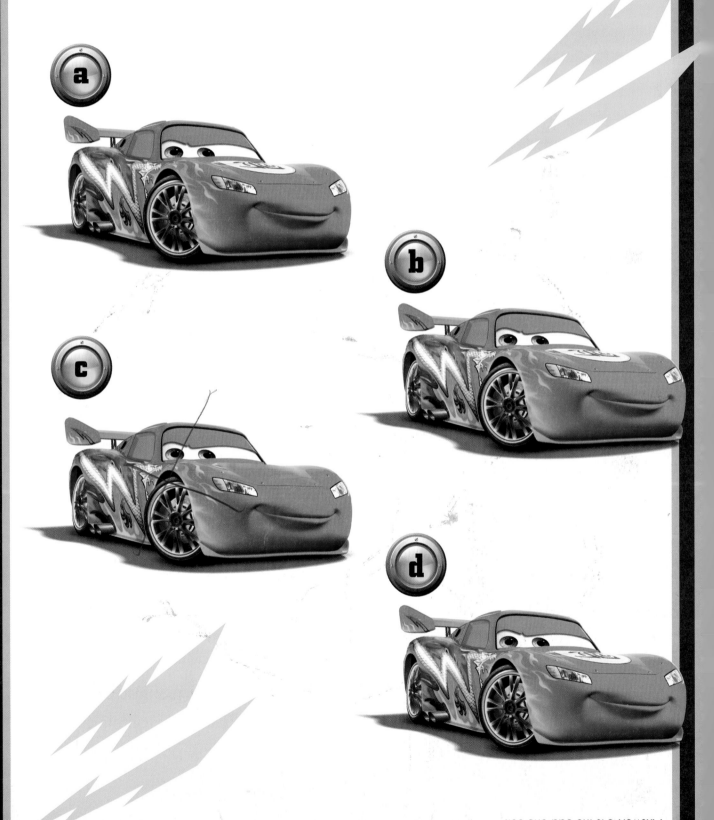

Mater's makeover

1. One day, Lightning McQueen's friends were admiring his shiny paint job. "Did you get a polishin' today?" asked Mater.

2. "I sure did, Mater!" Lightning McQueen replied. "You look slick," Mater told his friend. "You know, I was shiny once too ... "

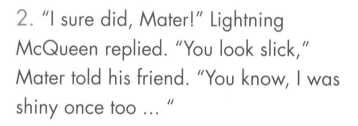

3. "You're just a little bit rusty, Mater," explained Lightning.
"My Rust-eze sponsors can fix that."
So, he raced off to arrange it.

4. Soon, Mater's rust had been taken care of by Rust-eze. Lightning then organised a wax polish to make Mater look as good as new!

5. The crowd cheered when Mater drove down Main Street. Everyone loved his shiny new look! Lightning was proud of his friend.

6. However, Mater felt silly with everyone watching him. He spoke in his best voice and avoided puddles because he was scared to get dirty!

7. "What's wrong?" Lightning asked, when Mater stopped beside a field. "I'd like to race in there," Mater said, "but then I'd mess up my polishin'."

8. Seeing how sad his friend was, Lightning opened the gate. "Wa-hoo!" Mater shouted, as he sped around, leaving a messy trail behind him.

9. It didn't take long for Mater to look like his old self again. "I may not be shiny on the outside," he cheered, "but I sure feel like I am on the inside!"

10. Lightning smiled. He was glad to see his friend happy again. "And that's where it matters most," he laughed, joining Mater in the mud!

The end

About the story

1 What was everyone admiring about Lightning?

2 Who are Lightning McQueen's sponsors?

3 What did Mater avoid because he was scared to get dirty?

4 Who joined Mater in the mud?

Answers: 1) His shiny paint job. 2) Rust-eze. 3) Puddles. 4) Lightning McQueen.

Search the shop

Ramone needs four things before he can give Lightning McQueen a new paint job. Can you help him find each object from the panel?

Tick a box when you spot each object.

Doc's garage

Doc Hudson is in his garage. Why don't you join him and answer these three teasers?

1 What does the big newspaper clipping say Doc was?

2 How many red books can you count in Doc's garage?

3 Can you spot three Piston Cups? Colour this cup when you've spotted them all!

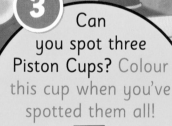

Answers: 1) A champion. 2) 7 red books. 3) The cups are in a tyre, on the table and near the boxes.

Dusty differences

Lightning is racing Doc across the dusty desert!
Can you find five changes in the bottom picture?

Colour a lightning bolt when you spot a difference!

Answers: 1) Sheriff has appeared in the picture. 2) Lightning's little lightning bolt is a different colour. 3) There are more dust clouds. 4) A cactus is missing. 5) The 95 is on Lightning's other headlight.

Hanging out

McQueen and Sally are chilling out with Fillmore. Join them and answer these cool questions!

1 Where is this flower on Fillmore's tent? Circle it when you find it!

2 What word is written on Fillmore?

3 What colour is Sally? Colour in the correct box below.

Red Blue

4 Which of these barrels is not part of a matching pair?

a b c d e f g

Colour in McQueen!

Answers: 1) the flower is above the pink lamp. 2) PEACE. 3) Blue. 4) c.

Pit stop pals

Lightning loves having Guido on his pit crew!
Give the pals some colour.

What is Lightning's
racing number? Write
your answer in the box.

Answer: 95.

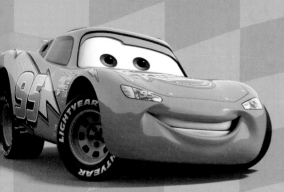

Cars code

Use the grid below to crack the code in the panel and find Lightning's catchphrase. The first letter has been found for you.

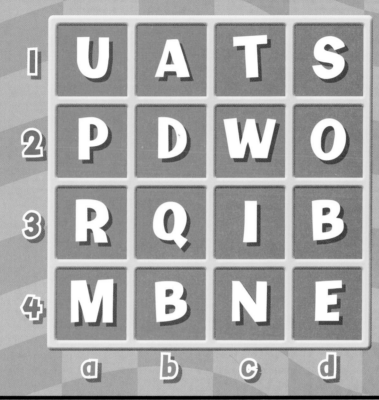

	a	b	c	d
1	U	A	T	S
2	P	D	W	O
3	R	Q	I	B
4	M	B	N	E

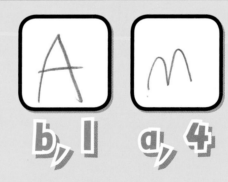

I   A   M

c, 3   b, 1   a, 4

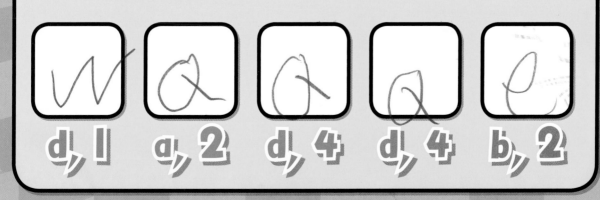

d, 1   a, 2   d, 4   d, 4   b, 2

Answer: I AM SPEED.

Pit puzzles

Lightning McQueen and Chick Hicks are taking a break from the big race! Can you answer these questions to help them get back on the track?

1 Which poster has more red cars?

a)

b)

PISTON CUP

PISTON CUP

2 Who is having his wheel replaced?

Answers: 1) b. 2) Chick Hicks. 3) The hose nozzles are a different shape; the circles are a different colour; there are three stars on the left pump and two on the right pump. 4) a - 4, b - 2, c - 1, d - 3. 5) b.

3 Can you spot the three differences between the petrol pumps?

4 Can you match the spanners on the floor with their place in the toolbox?

5 Which oil can doesn't appear in the big picture? Tick the box.

a
b
c
d

Lightning's cones

What does Lightning like doing best?
Follow the cones on the track to find out,
then spell out the word in the boxes below.

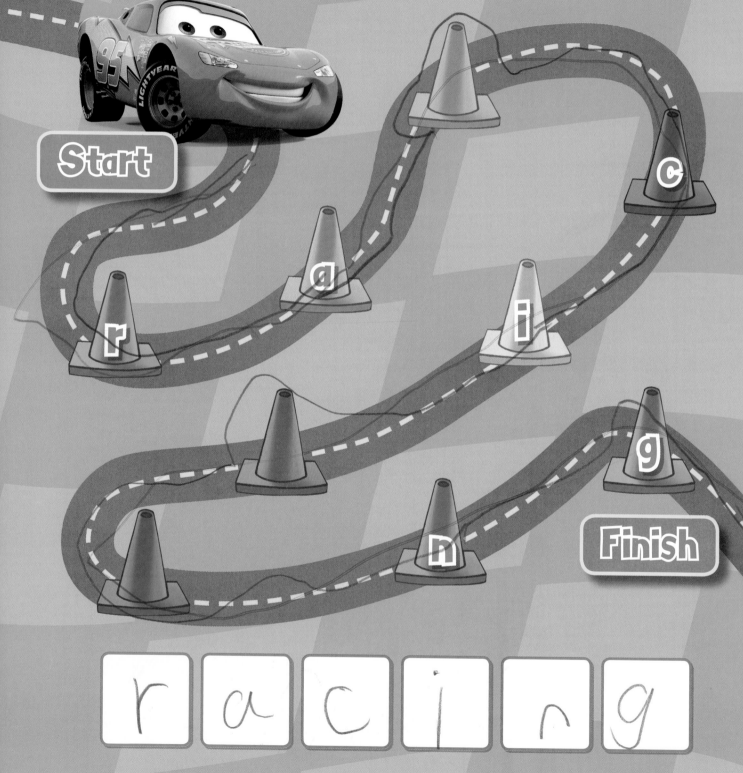

| r | a | c | i | n | g |

Mud splats!

Racing around has made these cars muddy! Can you answer the questions before they get cleaned up?

1 Which car has the most mud splats?

Sheriff

Fillmore

Doc

Lightning

2 Which car has no mud splats?

Sally

Colour Sally's mud splats blue to make them disappear!

Answers: 1) Lightning has the most with nine mud splats . 2) Sheriff has no mud splats.

Race game

Will you be the first to collect all your cups in this cool Cars game?

You will need

A dice, two counters and some crayons.

Start

WINNER

The crowd cheers you on! Throw again!

You get new tyres! Move on 1 space.

You spin off the track! Go back 1 space.

How to play

1 This game is for two players. Decide who will be player one and who will be player two.

2 Take it in turns to roll the dice and move around the board, following any instructions you land on.

3 If you land on a space with a Piston Cup, colour one of the cups on your player card.

4 Keep moving around the board until one player has coloured in all of their cups – they are the winner!

You burst a tyre! Miss a go.

You're out of fuel! Go back 2 spaces.

Drift Lightning McQueen

Give Lightning McQueen a flash
of winning colour.